Herbal D-Tox

Cookbook for Cleansing

Published by Wild Rose Enterprises
Surrey, British Columbia, Canada

Distributed by Christmas Natural Foods
Surrey, British Columbia, Canada

First printing, February 1996
Printed in Canada on Recycled Paper

Design by Wyndehorse Communications
White Rock, British Columbia, Canada

Table of Contents

Wild Rose Herbal D-Tox 4
Why Cleansing is So Important 5
Why the Wild Rose Herbal D-Tox? 8
Foods to Avoid 10
Foods to Enjoy 13
Wild Rose Meal Plan — Charts 16
Candida Diet 19

Recipes for Cleansing

Breakfast

New Ideas 25

Desserts

Simple Recipes 27

Dressings

Oil and Lemon 28
Tahini Salad Dressing 28
Substitute Caesar Salad Dressing 29
Salsa 30
Guacamole 31

Salads

Chop Suey Salad 32
Sesame Cucumber Salad 32
Crabmeat and Avocado Salad 33
Bean Sprout Salad 34
Spinach Salad 35
Fish Salad 36
Stuffed Tomatoes 37
Turkey Salad with Rice 38
Confetti Salad 39

Soups

Vegetable Chowder 40
Barley Soup 41
Fresh Beet Borcht 42
Peasant Vegetable Soup 43
Spinach Soup 44
Zucchini Soup 45
Turkey Vegetable Soup 46
Bouillabaisse 47
Hearty Alaska Cod Chowder 48

Main Events

Spinach Casserole 49
Nut Loaf 50
Three-Bean Loaf 51
Lentil Dhal 52
Pulao Rice 53
Golden Saffron Rice 54
Frijoles (Refried Beans) 55
Hot Sauce 56
Curried Lentils 58
Savoury Beans 59
Blushed Cauliflower 60
Sophisticated Vegetables 61
Neapolitan Zucchini 62
Gado-Gado Sauce 63
Hurry-Up Hash Patties 64
Falafel 65
Sunflower Seed Wedge 66
Veggie Nut Loaf 67
Millet Sunflower Carrot Casserole 68
Baked Stuffed Fish 69
Lemon Broiled Chicken 70
Curried Turkey Thighs 71
Fish Fillets Almandine 72
Herbed Baked Fish Steak 73
Cooking Grains 74

ild Rose Herbal D-tox Kit

Our cars usually run best on a twice-yearly tune ups...and so do our bodies. Body "tune-ups" means cleansing — the well-established corner stone of wholistic physical maintenance. Since the early days, medicine practitioners and simple common sense have recommended spring and fall cleanses. Many people also like to cleanse after festive seasons, to either shed a few extra pounds or to undo some of the effects of over-consumption.

Wild Rose Herbal D-Tox Kit

hy Cleansing Is So Important

During the daily process of body maintenance our bodies are continuously building new cells and breaking down old cells. Most of these broken down materials are recycled, however, little by little an accumulation of toxins builds up in the system. Materials that are not easily recycled and not easily removed can be eliminated simply with an organized cleansing program.

In 1958, a mere 419 pounds of the few known additives at that time were added to foods in North America. Today there are over 3 million additives with almost 2 billion pounds added to our food chain each year, and this number appears to be growing. It is estimated that our daily per capita additive consumption is 15 to 20 grams per year...that's over 10% of our body weight. Since these additives have not been naturally consumed in our genetic history we do not have efficient eliminative methods for them. Therefore, as never before, there is a strong need to systematically cleanse the body at least twice a year.

Most of this unwanted material is deposited in our digestive tract, colon, liver, lymphatic system and kidneys. There have been many health problems attributed to these toxic accumulations. Some feel that most of our modern societies' serious diseases can be postponed, reduced in severity or even eradicated by cleansing. The old saying, *"A stitch in time saves nine"*, is applicable here.

Cleansaherb: formulated to cleanse the bloodstream, muscle and lymphatic tissue of toxins.

Understandably, our systems can be taxed during the process of eliminating of these accumulated toxins. This is why straight fasting is not always the best choice when cleansing. Fasting often causes dramatic emotional and physical fluctuations and should *only* be done under the direction of a qualified health practitioner. One time-tested solution is to ease the body through a cleanse with the assistance of herbal preparations. By using herbal formulas to cleanse the liver, lymphatic system, digestive system, colon and to support the kidneys, the cleanse can be quicker, more thorough and easier to undergo. This traditional solution also enables one to eat a healthy and hearty diet while cleansing.

CL Herbal Extract: blood and lymphatic tissue detoxifier and bile flow stimulator.

During a cleanse one often experiences more bowel movements and increased urination. Although not common, some people experience what is called a *cleansing or healing crisis*. During a healing crisis one may experience mild flu-like symptoms as some of the heavy toxic accumulations are eliminated. This is usually considered a positive sign. It is better to rid the body of toxins than to let them accumulate further into disease problems in the future.

Biliherb: *useful for stimulating bile flow, detoxifing the liver and supporting spleen function.*

As the cleanse comes to an end one usually feels lighter, healthier and cleaner. After one or two cleanses over a period of several months they become very simple; taking a few cleansing supplements and following a special meal plan for twelve days becomes an enjoyable routine. By cleansing often, the smaller embedded accumulation of toxins will be removed, making each cleanse easier and more effective. It is not suggested to cleanse more than once every two months unless under the care of a practitioner.

Laxaherb: *a non-addictive short-term laxative formulated to tone the intestinal wall.*

hy the Wild Rose Herbal D-Tox ?

The Wild Rose Herbal D-Tox is a proven 12-day cleansing program that follows a healthy and satisfying meal plan. The Wild Rose D-Tox program eases the body through a cleanse by using herbal preparations that act on the liver, blood and lymphatic system, digestive tract and colon, while maintaining support for the kidneys.

The Wild Rose Herbal D-Tox is simple to use and both young and old receive excellent benefits. With the maintenance of a hearty diet, this program can be enjoyed by both novice and experienced cleansers. The experienced cleanser especially will notice the dramatic health benefits that are offered without the emotional and physical fluctuations that are often associated with fasting. The simple and self-explanatory meal plan included in the D-Tox kit combines 20% acidic forming foods and 80% neutral and alkaline forming foods. The column headings on the meal plan indicate that the foods listed in each column naturally turn into ash, acid or become neutral once they are inside the digestive tract. The easy to follow chart lists all foods that may or may not be eaten.

Many people find they lose weight over the 12-day cleansing period, and if they choose to continue the Wild Rose meal plan they will often continue to lose weight. The Wild Rose meal plan is a time-tested meal program that does not have to be mundane. In fact, over 95% of the world's population eats these types of foods every day. Most of the foods listed on the meal plan are low fat, high fibre foods that are rich in vitamins, minerals and antioxidants. You are encouraged to take this opportunity to experiment with foods from other lands; buy a new ethnic cook book and try new spices and herbs. This will give you the opportunity to make your meals delicious...even gourmet. Many of the spices and herbs may sound exotic but most ethnic grocery stores and health food stores carry them as regular stock.

Foods to Avoid -- Candida & the Herbal D-tox

Acid, Alkaline and Neutral Forming Foods

The column headings on the meal plan indicate whether the foods listed in each column naturally turn into ash (alkaline), acid or become neutral once they are inside the digestive tract.

Regarding Candida

The Wild Rose Herbal D-Tox program is also suited to eliminating excess Candida. Like all yeasts Candida thrives on a diet rich in simple carbohydrates, so all sweets and refined foods must be avoided. Candida also grows on all yeasts, molds, fungi and fermented foods. One should do away with foods containing these elements as well as nutritional yeast or supplements with yeast in them. This means no mushrooms, grapes (including raisins), or oranges — as yeast naturally occurs on the skins of these foods. (see Candida Diet on Page 19)

Fermented Foods

This also means no wine, beer or other fermented drinks — as yeast is a main ingredient. No vinegar, soy sauce, black tea, misó or tofu — these are also fermented foods. The reason black tea is "out" is because it is fermented during the process of making it. Green tea, although it is the same species of plant, is fine because it is not fermented.

 Healthier Cleansing Tip: *Herbal teas are a great "pick me up" when doing a cleanse.*

Flour

All flour breads and flour products such as pasta, cakes, pancakes, flour in sauces and crackers must be eliminated. Flour products are not recommended due to the glue-like substance created when flour is mixed with water. This substance has a tendency to stick to the lining of the intestinal tract and foods that may congest your system during a detox should be avoided.

Coffee

If one drinks coffee regularly, a small amount can be enjoyed during the 12-day program. Two cups maximum daily. Large amounts can weaken the immune system and over time can also cause stress to the adrenal glands.

Nuts

Peanuts, which are grow under ground, must be avoided as they contain some naturally occurring yeasts and molds. The rest of the nut family are fine to eat.

 Healthier Cleansing Tip: *Many people who enjoy peanut butter have found almond or cashew butter or tahini on rice cakes is a great substitute.*

Sugar, Dried Fruit, Fresh Fruit and Fruit Juices

Sugar and dried fruit are to be avoided because yeast finds them a most acceptable food to grow on, and ridding the body of excess yeast is one of the functions of the Herbal Detox. While on the Herbal Detox a bit of fruit can be eaten (see under columns on Page 19). The sweeter the fruit the worse it is, which means that fruits like bananas, melons and pineapples should not be eaten. Fruit juices, whether naturally or white sugar sweetened, all contain large amounts of natural sugars and should be avoided while on the Herbal Detox. Remember to read labels carefully when buying foods, if you do not usually do this you will be surprised at the large amount of even "healthy" packaged foods that contain added sugar.

Foods To Enjoy -- The Basics of the Herbal D-Tox Meal Plan

Acid, Alkaline and Neutral Forming Foods

Remember that the column headings on the meal plan indicate that the foods listed in each column naturally turn into ash, acid or become neutral once they are inside the digestive tract.

Vegetables

The vegetables can be eaten cooked (lightly steamed is preferable) or raw. A good salad dressing is simply fresh lemon juice, oil and spices.

Grains -- Unrefined Grains

Grains must be whole grains, not the flour of the grain, or foods that contain flour (see previous information on flour). Most grains are quite acceptable to eat unless one has an allergy to a certain grain. The following (in descending order) are the best grains for the diet: millet, buckwheat, brown rice, rye, cornmeal, seven grain cereal, Red River cereal, oatmeal, wheat.

And to a smaller extent:

Legumes

Too many legumes, such as beans, in the diet can sometimes cause excessive gas and discomfort. Most illnesses accompany digestive problems. Therefore, foods that cause difficult digestion should be eaten only occasionally. Recommend two to three servings of legumes per week.

Some Fruit

The sweeter the fruit is the worse it is, suggesting that fruits like bananas, melons and pineapple should not be eaten. This means no tropical fruit, only one serving of domestic fruit per day allowed; apples, pears, peaches, plums and berries. See columns on Page xx.

Meat

Preferably organic chicken and wild fish. Please note that meat has been included in the Meal Plan as it is understood that not all people are vegetarians.

 Healthier Cleansing Tip: It is becoming increasingly well established that a diet rich in fruits, vegetables, grains and legumes with less red meats can be healthier in the long term.

Water

Water is important while on the Herbal D-tox program. Remember to drink either spring or reverse osmosis water (not tap water), or herbal teas while cleansing. Rather than recommending a maximum number of glasses per day, simply drink when thirsty, making sure that at least two 8 oz glasses per day are consumed. Liquids will help to flush the toxins from your body.

Healthier Cleansing Tip: Drinking plenty of water everyday is excellent for all round flushing of the body whether cleansing or not.

In Conclusion...

At first this might appear to leave very little to eat but your diet can be quite exciting and creative. To help make your cleanse easier and more enjoyable, we have included a wide selection of recipes.

Wild Rose Meal Plan

Eat less than 20 % of your diet from this column.

Column 1
Protein Foods -- Acid Forming

Most Recommended:

Fish (eat all you want even if over 20% of total diet)

Acceptable During Program:

Beans (dried)	Peas (dried)
Beef	Poultry
Coffee (Black- maximum	Pork
two cups per day)	Prunes (cooked)
Eggs (whole)	Rhubarb (cooked)
Lamb	Rice (white)
Lentils	Soy Beans
Liver	Tea (black)
Nuts (except almonds and	Veal
Brazil nuts ~80%; see	Wheat Germ
column 2)	Whole Grains (most)

Not Recommended:

Buttermilk	Seafood (shell fish)
Cheese (natural)	Yogurt

Foods with Acid, Alkaline or Neutral Properties

Eat 80% or more of your diet from both columns 2 and 3 combined.

Column 2
Starch Foods -- Alkaline Forming

Most Recommended:

Almonds	Millet
Brown Rice	Buckwheat

Acceptable During Program:

Apples	Popcorn
Apricots	Potatoes (baked)
Berries	Pumpkin - Squash
Brazil Nuts	Sesame Seeds
Cherries	Tahini
Peaches/Pears/Plums	Tomatoes (fresh)

Not Recommended During Program:

Bananas	Melons
Cantaloupe	Molasses
Currants	Pasta (i.e. macaroni,
Dates and Figs	spaghetti)
Fruit Juice (natural)	Pineapple
Flour (white)	Raisins
Grapes	Soups (thick)
Honey and Maple Syrup	Tropical Fruit

Not Recommended at Any Time:

Cakes, Candy, Ice Cream	Jams and Jellies
Cereal (processed)	Oily Nuts and Peanuts
Flour Gravy	Pies and Pastries
Fruit Juice with sugar	Sugar (white or brown)
Pop/Soda	*(continued)*

Foods with Acid, Alkaline or Neutral Properties

Eat 80% or more of your diet from both columns 2 and 3 combined.

Column 3
Neutral Foods -- Bulk Forming

Most Recommended:

Chives	Onions
Garlic	Water

Acceptable During Program:

Arugula	Green Beans/Green Peas
Artichokes	Green or Red Peppers
Asparagus	Kale
Avocado	Kohlrabi
Beets or Beet Tops	Lettuce
Broccoli	Mustard Greens
Brussel Sprouts	Okra
Butter	Olive Oil
Cabbage	Parsley
Carrots	Parsnips
Celery	Peppermint
Collard	Radiccio
Corn	Radishes
Cucumbers	Rutabagas
Dandelion	Sorrel
Eggplant	Spinach
Endive	Turnips
Escarole	Water Cress

Not Recommended During Program:

Cottage Cheese	Mushrooms

andida Diet

For your interest we have included information about Dr. Willard's Candida diet. This is a diet that one can follow immediately after the 12-day detox program.

This following program has been very successful in combating Candida (yeast) colonization. The program should last for three to nine months, unless otherwise advised by a health practitioner. This program must be adhered to more strictly than most, as "cheating" will only create a stronger strain of Candida in your body.

There are three basic components to the program:

1. Eliminating the foods that Candida lives on. This is the hardest, yet the most important, part.

2. Inhibiting Candida with specific vitamins and destroying them with homeopathic remedies.

3. Strengthening the body so that the Candida will not return.

(continued)

Food and Drinks to be Avoided

- All flour products (for 1 to 2 months)

- All dairy products (for 1 to 2 months, butter is acceptable)

- Any flour product with yeast (entire length of program)

- Any curded or fermented dairy (after 1-1/2 months yogurt is acceptable)

- All yeast or yeast-containing foods

- No peanuts, grapes, oranges, mushrooms, tropical fruits or melons.

- No wine, beer or vinegar (including sauces with vinegar; after 2 months vinegar is acceptable)

- No soya sauce, miso, tofu (after 1-1/2 months these are acceptable)

- No sugar or sweetening agent of any kind

- No dried fruit

- No tea (herbal teas, including green tea, are acceptable)

- Only one piece of fruit daily, two cups of coffee (maximum), two ounces of distilled alcohol per week (if desired)

Good Foods

At first this might appear to leave very little to eat. Much of this feeling is due to cravings which you have had all along. On this program you can eat the following good foods:

- All the vegetables desired (except mushrooms)

- Meat (if desired; organic chicken and wild fish are best)

- Grains (flours of the grain are not acceptable, but the whole grains themselves are)

- Beans (not more than three times per week)

- Some fruit (apples, pears, peaches, plums and berries; no more than the mass of an average-sized apple per day)

Supplements

- Homeopathic Candida 30X (5-10 drops per day)

- BEVC (2 tablets, twice daily)

- Digestive Enzymes (1-3 capsules with each meal)

- After 1-1/2 months, add a high potency Acidophilus (2 capsules twice daily)

Notes to Remember...

_____

_____

_____

_____

_____

_____

_____

_____

_____

_____

_____

_____

_____

_____

_____

_____

_____

_____

Tasty Recipes

...to Enhance your 12-Day Herbal D-Tox Program

Notes to Remember...

_____

_____

_____

_____

_____

_____

_____

_____

_____

_____

_____

_____

_____

_____

_____

_____

_____

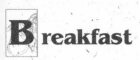reakfast

A word about breakfast...

A popular question we hear about the Wild Rose Herbal D-Tox kit is, "What can I eat for breakfast?". Well, even when you take flour and breads out of your diet for a few days there are many simple, quick ways of preparing foods for breakfast. We have listed a few ideas here, and with a little imagination and experimentation you will create your own combinations for a healthy and fulfilling way to the start the day.

1. It goes without saying that the old steadfast — oatmeal — is one of the healthiest breakfasts around. You can choose rolled or steel-cut oats. (See *Cooking Grains* at the back of the book.) You may add chopped apples, one to two teaspoons of vanilla (adds a natural sweetness) and cinnamon to the oats while cooking for additional flavour.

2. You can top rice cakes with tahini, almond or cashew butter. For variation and crunch you can sprinkle them with sesame or sunflower seeds.

3. Brown rice or millet, cooked with apples, vanilla (see #1 above) and cinnamon, is a delicious alternative to cooked oats.

Breakfast -- *continued*

4. Try cooking other grains or combination of grains (see *Cooking Grains*) and topping them with mashed peaches, strawberries, chopped apples and other fruits that are listed under column 2 on the meal plan.

5. Leftover hot cereals can be moulded into the bottom of a cake pan and placed in the refrigerator to solidify for a few hours — or overnight. Take it out and cut it into squares. Cook the squares in a little butter and sprinkle with chopped nuts, seeds, cinnamon and chopped apples or pears.

6. Juice your own apples, strawberries, pears, etc and pour a little (1/2 cup) on your oatmeal or cooked grains for a yummy, moist addition.

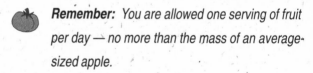 **Remember:** *You are allowed one serving of fruit per day — no more than the mass of an average-sized apple.*

Desserts

Needless to say, a detox program greatly restricts desserts from a meal plan. The only safe dessert that one can have while on the detox program is fresh domestic fruit (remember that no tropical fruit is allowed on this program). Domestic fruit is mostly restricted to apples, peaches, pears, plums and berries. You are allowed one serving of fruit per day, one serving is no more than the mass of an average-sized apple.

1. Baked Apple — try a baked apple for dessert, just like grandma might have made! Simply core an apple, place it in a baking dish and sprinkle some cinnamon, vanilla and lemon juice into the centre. Cover with tin foil and bake in the oven for 10 to 15 minutes, depending on the type of apple (longer for the harder Granny Smith-type apples). A simple but delicious dessert!

2. Fresh Fruit — serve fresh sliced domestic fruit into a dessert bowl. You can also sprinkle fresh lemon juice, cinnamon, chopped nuts or sunflower seeds over it. Yum!

ressings

Oil and Lemon

1/2 cup	oil (virgin olive)
1/2 cup	fresh lemon juice
to taste	red or black pepper
optional	Spike (a spice mix available in most health food stores)

1. *Mix all ingredients and store in refrigerator.*

Tahini Salad Dressing

4-5 tbsp	lemon or lime juice
1 tsp each	oregano, tarragon, basil, kelp powder, thyme
1 tsp	minced fresh garlic
1 tsp	salt
1/2 tsp	cayenne pepper
1/2 cup	tahini
1 cup	oil (virgin olive)

1. *Mix all ingredients and store in refrigerator.*

Substitute Caesar Salad Dressing

1	egg yolk
lots	crushed garlic (2 to 6 cloves, depending upon your taste)
6 tsp	fresh lemon juice
1/2 cup	olive oil
to taste	pepper and salt
optional	chopped anchovies.

1. In a large bowl, whisk the egg yolk with the crushed garlic, a little lemon juice and then slowly add the olive oil while continuing to whisk.

2. Add rest of lemon juice, then add pepper, salt and optional anchovies to taste.

3. Toss with your favourite mix of salad greens.

Salsa

A tasty topping for almost any dish: rice, fish, meat, nut loaf, grilled veggies, etc...

You can add a variety of vegetables, and even fruits, to zest up a salsa. Start with a base of fresh tomatoes, onions and peppers then add your choice of accompaniments.

Main Ingredients

1 cup	fresh tomatoes, diced
1/2 cup	red onions, diced
1/4 cup	red bell pepper, diced
1/4 cup	green bell pepper, diced
1/4 cup	olive oil
2 tbsp	lemon juice

Additional Options

1/4 cup	green onions, chopped
2 tbsp	cilantro, chopped fine
1/4 cup	fresh peached, diced
1 clove	garlic, minced
1	jalapeno, minced
to taste	ground black pepper
to taste	salt
to taste	ground cumin

Putting your Salsa together...

1. *Toss the main ingredients with others of your choice from the additional options list.*

2. *Serve with any meal for extra added zest.*

Guacamole

...a Mexican favourite

2	large avocado, peeled and mashed
1	tomato, chopped
2	cloves garlic, crushed
2	jalapeno peppers, chopped
1 tsp	fresh lemon juice

1. *Toss all ingredients and serve as a side dish to a salad or with rice.*

Tip: Keep the avocado pit in the dip to help prevent discoloration and store in the refrigerator.

alads

Chop Suey Salad

Serves 10

2 lb	raw bean sprouts
5-6	stalks of celery, finely shredded
3-4	green onions, chopped
3-4	large green peppers, chopped
3	large carrots, thinly sliced
3/4 cup	bamboo shoots

1. Mix all above ingredients in large bowl and toss with 3/4 cup of dressing. (see Dressings)

Sesame Cucumber Salad

Serves 6

2 med	cucumbers, peeled, sliced very thin
1/2 tsp	salt
1 cup	dressing of choice (see Dressings)
1/4 cup	toasted sesame seeds
2 tbsp	chives, minced
	mixed salad greens

1. Toast sesame seeds in a skillet for 1-2 minutes over medium-low heat, stirring constantly.

2. Mix the cucumber, salt, dressing, sesame seeds and chives together.

3. Chill, then toss with your favourite mixture of salad greens.

Crabmeat and Avocado Salad

Serves 6 to 8

1/2 cup	crabmeat
1/3 cup	celery, chopped
3	hard-boiled eggs, chopped
2 tbsp	pimento, chopped
1 tbsp	green or red onions, chopped
1/2 tsp	salt
1/2 cup	dressing of choice (see Dressings)
3	large avocados
to taste	fresh lemon juice
to taste	salt
3 tbsp	finely chopped nuts
1 tsp	melted butter
2 tbsp	slivered almonds

1. Mix together the crabmeat, celery, eggs, pimento, onions, salt and dressing.

2. Cut unpeeled avocados lengthwise in half. Remove pits.

3. Brush halves with lemon juice, sprinkle lightly with salt then fill with crabmeat mix.

4. Toss chopped nuts and melted butter together. Spoon over crab.

5. Place in a baking dish. Bake in a 400° F oven for 10 minutes.

6. Remove from oven. Sprinkle with slivered almonds and bake 5 minutes longer.

Bean Sprout Salad

A light and refreshing accompaniment...

Serves 3 to 4

1/2 lb	bean sprouts (i.e. mung beans)
3	green onions, cut diagonally in 1/2" lengths
4	radishes, thinly sliced
1/3	cucumber, unpeeled, thinly sliced diagonally
1/2 lb	green beans, sliced diagonally
2-3 tbsp	dressing of choice (see Dressings)

1. Rinse the bean sprouts. Blanch them in boiling water for 3 minutes. Drain in colander.

2. Immediately dip colander in large pan of ice water to stop the cooking process. Stir gently with a fork.

3. When cold remove colander from water and let drain. Turn onto double thickness of paper towelling and drain thoroughly.

4. Mix sprouts with the green onions, radishes, cucumber and green beans. Chill.

5. When ready to serve, toss with 2 to 3 tablespoons of one of above dressings, according to taste.

Spinach Salad
...tasty and full of iron

Serves 4 to 6

1 tbsp	chives, chopped (If chives not available then green onions may be used)
2 tbsp	leeks, diced
1/2 cup	olives, chopped
2 - 8 oz	bunches fresh, young spinach washed and chilled
to taste	dressing of your choice (see Dressings)
1	hard boiled egg, chopped (optional)

1. Mince chives, leeks and olives together until very fine and pulpy.

2. Add the dressing of your choice and let stand for 20 to 30 minutes to blend the flavours.

3. Tear the spinach into bite size pieces. Pour dressing mixture over the spinach. Add optional chopped hard boiled egg.

4. Toss and serve.

Fish Salad

Mixed with herbs and garlic spice up this tasty fish salad.

Serves 4 to 6

1 lb	firm white fish fillets, poached, drained, and chilled
1/2 cup	dressing of your choice (see under Dressings)
1/4 cup	green or red onion, chopped
2	cloves garlic, minced
1 bunch	radishes, sliced thinly
1 tsp	your choice — dill, oregano, basil...
1/3 cup	olive oil or your choice
1/2 cup	cucumber, chopped
1/2 cup	string beans, chopped

1. *Cut fish into bite-sized cubes. Marinate with the dressing of your choice.*

2. *While fish is marinating toss the onion, garlic, radishes, herbs, oil, cucumber and beans together.*

3. *Serve the mixed vegetables over the fish, with a side dish of rice.*

Stuffed Tomatoes

A perfect accompaniment for Fish Fillet
Almandine with a side dish of rice.

Serves 6

3/4 cup	chopped nuts or seeds
6	large firm tomatoes
1 tsp	salt
1 cup	parsley, chopped
1/2 cup	green onions, chopped
1/4 cup	fresh mint, finely chopped (or 1 tsp dried mint)
1/2 cup	olive oil or oil of your choice
1/4 cup	fresh lemon juice
1/4 tsp	fresh ground pepper
	lettuce leaves, lemon wedges

1. *Core tomatoes. Cut slice off stem ends, reserving slices for later. Scoop out centre over bowl, leaving a firm shell. Sprinkle insides with 1/2 tsp salt; invert on paper towelling for 30 minutes to drain.*

2. *Chop tomato pulp (no seed) coarsely.*

3. *Mix chopped pulp, parsley, green onion, mint, vegetable oil, lemon juice, remaining 1/2 tsp salt and pepper. Add to nuts/seeds; toss gently.*

4. *Spoon nut mix into tomato shells, mounding slightly. Top each with tomato slice; garnish with sprigs of mint. Arrange on lettuce-lined salad platter. Garnish with lemon wedges and serve.*

Turkey Salad with Rice

The rich flavour of curry makes this a delicious salad...

Serves 4

1 cup	cooked turkey or chicken, cubed (preferably organic)
2 cups	cooked rice or millet, chilled (or substitute chopped nuts or seeds)
1 cup	celery, diced
1	medium green pepper, shredded
2 tbsp	pimento, chopped
2 tbsp	parsley, chopped
1/2 cup	sunflower or olive oil
1/3 cup	fresh lemon juice
1/2 tsp	curry powder, good and fresh

1. Mix and chill the turkey or chicken, rice or millet, celery, green pepper, pimento and parsley.

2. In another bowl, combine the oil, lemon juice and curry and let stand for one hour.

3. Pour over turkey/rice mixture just before serving.

Confetti Salad

...a colourful salad for a sunny day

Serves 4 to 6

2 med	young cucumbers, cubed
2 med	ripe tomatoes, cubed
1/2 cup	sliced radishes
2 minced	scallions, include green part
1 med	red bell pepper, minced
1 med	green bell pepper, minced
1/2 cup	spanish or red onion, minced
1/2 cup	finely minced fresh parsley, packed
1/4 cup	olive oil
juice	from 1 large lemon
to taste	salt and pepper

1. *Toss together gently and chill. You can make this several hours ahead of serving time.*

oups

Vegetable Chowder

...hot and hearty for cool days

Serves 6 to 8

2 cups	carrots, sliced
1 cup	celery, sliced
2 cups	potatoes, diced
1 cup	water
to taste	salt

Cook the above for 10 to 12 minutes.

1 cup	squash, cooked and mashed
1 cup	potatoes, mashed
1/4 tsp	nutmeg
1/2 tsp	ginger
1/8 tsp	mace
to taste	pepper

1. Mix mashed squash and mashed potatoes.

2. Add seasoning to mashed potato/ squash mixture, then add to cooked carrots, celery, potatoes and their stock.

3. Heat for a few minutes and stir. Do Not Boil.

4. Serve with sprig of fresh parsley or other favourite herb.

Barley Soup

...a traditional soup, rich in flavour

Serves 4 to 6

2	onions, chopped
4	carrots, chopped
1	small turnip, chopped
4 stalks	celery, chopped
1-2	potatoes, chopped
4 tsp	butter
1 cup	barley
7 cups	water
4-1/2 cups	fresh tomatoes, chopped
to taste	parsley, vegetable salt or Spike

1. Sauté the onions, carrots, turnips, celery and potatoes in the butter until onions are transparent.

2. Add water and tomatoes, bring to a boil, then add barley. Cover and simmer for 1-1/2 to 2 hours.

3. Garnish with parsley and serve hot.

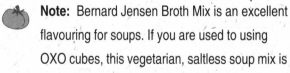 **Note:** Bernard Jensen Broth Mix is an excellent flavouring for soups. If you are used to using OXO cubes, this vegetarian, saltless soup mix is an excellent alternative.

Fresh Beet Borscht

...great for strengthening the blood

Serves 8 to 10

1	medium onion, chopped
1	garlic clove, minced
1	turnip, diced
1 lb	fresh beets, shredded
1 tbsp	fresh lemon juice
1/4 tsp	salt
10 cups	broth
1 lb	yellow squash, sliced
3 cups	cabbage, shredded

1. Combine onion, garlic, turnip and fresh beets in a large saucepan, simmer for 30 minutes.

2. Add yellow squash and cabbage to the simmering mixture, and simmer another 30 minutes.

3. Serve this soup hot, and garnish with a favourite herb, i.e. dill weed or parsley.

Peasant Vegetable Soup

Winter vegetables cooked with grains make a warming meal...

Serves 8 to 10

3	leeks, chopped
1 bunch	bok choy, chopped
3 tbsp	oil or butter
8 cups	water
1	bay leaf
2 cups	fresh zucchini
1/4 cup	amaranth (ancient grain of the Aztecs), or barley
1 cup	asparagus pieces
1 cup	peas
1 cup	spinach, chopped
to taste	salt

1. *Sauté the leeks in oil or butter, add the bok choy, water, bay leaf, zucchini, amaranth, asparagus, peas.*

2. *Cook covered over low heat for 30 minutes, or until the amaranth is done.*

3. *Add the spinach and cook 5 minutes more.*

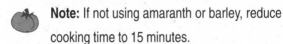 **Note:** If not using amaranth or barley, reduce cooking time to 15 minutes.

Spinach Soup

Flavourful and rich in nutrients...

Serves 4 to 6

4 cups	water
2 bunches	spinach, washed and chopped
2 tbsp	oil
1/2 cup	leeks, thinly sliced
1/2 cup	ground nuts of your choice
1 tsp	curry powder
1 cup	your choice of cooked beans
to taste	salt

1. *Bring water to a boil. Add the spinach and simmer for 5 to 7 minutes.*

2. *Sauté the leeks in the oil and then add to the spinach.*

3. *Add the ground nuts, curry powder and cooked beans and stir.*

4. *Heat thoroughly and serve.*

Zucchini Soup

...something new for that bountiful harvest of summer garden zucchini.

Serves 6 to 8

3 lbs	zucchini, cut into chunks
1/4 lb	lean ham (organic), chopped
1 can	chicken broth, Bernard Jensen Broth Mix or seasoning vegetable mix
3-1/2 cups	water
1-1/2 tsp	salt
1/4 tsp	pepper
1/2 cup	chives or leeks

1. Combine all ingredients. Cook for 1 hour or until zucchini is tender.

2. Put in a blender and blend or you can put through a sieve.

3. Reheat and serve.

 Healthier Cleansing Tip: Adding grains to soups is a good way of ensuring that you get your daily allowance of health, nutrient and fibre-rich grains.

Turkey Vegetable Soup

...a light brothy soup

Serves 6

	boulion cubes.
2	turkey legs, skinned (2-1/2 lbs)
2	medium carrots, sliced
2	stalks celery with tops, sliced
2 tsp	salt
1/4 tsp	dried basil leaves
8 cups. 10 cups	water
19 oz. 1 cup	totomoes. onion, coarsely chopped
2 tbsp	oil
	barley. parsley, chopped
1 tsp.	pepper.

1. *Rinse turkey and place in a 24 cup (5.5 litre) saucepan.*

2. *Add the water, carrots, celery, salt and basil to the turkey, cover and bring to a boil.*

3. *Reduce heat, cover and simmer 1-1/2 hrs.*

4. *Sauté the onions in oil until golden and tender, add them to the soup.*

5. *Garnish the soup with the chopped parsley before serving.*

 Healthier Cleansing Tip: *Consider organic poultry and wild fish when cooking for health, to help to minimize your intake of toxins and the chemicals which are often fed to non-organic animals.*

Bouillabaisse

A simplified version of this traditional hearty fish soup.

Serves 4 to 6

2 lbs	fish
4 cups	water
1/2 cup	oil
2	onions, chopped
1 clove	garlic, crushed
pinch each	thyme, bay leaf, fennel
8 each	mussels and clams
1 cup each	lobster meat and shrimp, shelled
1/2 cup	pimentos, sliced
pinch	saffron

 Tip: Buy the freshest fish for the most flavour.

1. Simmer the cleaned fish until the water is reduced by half. Save the broth.

2. Cut the fish into serving pieces. Place the oil in a heavy soup pot. Add the onion, garlic, thyme, bay leaf and fennel.

3. Add the remaining fish broth, bring to a boil then boil rapidly for 5 minutes.

4. Add the fish, mussels, clams, lobster, shrimp and pimentos and simmer another 10 minutes.

5. Crumble the saffron into the soup and stir gently to distribute. Serve hot.

Hearty Alaska Cod Chowder
...Manhattan style

Serves 6

1-1/2 lbs	Alaska Cod fillets or other firm fish, thawed if necessary.
1 cup	onion, chopped
1 cup	zucchini, chopped
1 large	clove garlic, minced
1/4 cup	oil
4-1/2	fresh tomatoes, chopped
2 cups	tomato juice
1/3 cup	water
3/4 tsp	salt
3/4 tsp	crushed basil leaves
dash	hot pepper sauce (optional)

1. *Cut the fish into large chunks.*

2. *Sauté the onion, zucchini and garlic in the oil.*

3. *Add the tomatoes, tomato juice, water, salt, basil, optional hot sauce and heat to boiling.*

4. *Add the cod and simmer, covered, about 10 minutes or until fish flakes easily when tested with a fork.*

 Note: Recipe may be halved.

 ain Events

Spinach Casserole

...the perfect accompaniment for curried lentils and a salad of your choice.

Serves 2

1 cup	brown rice, cooked
2	eggs
2 tbsp	parsley
1/2 tsp	salt
1/2 tsp	red or black pepper
1 lb	fresh spinach, chopped
1/2 cup	wheat germ
2 tbsp	butter, melted

1. Combine rice with the eggs, parsley, salt and pepper. Stir in the spinach.

2. Pour into oiled casserole dish.

3. Combine the wheat germ and butter and sprinkle this mixture on top.

4. Bake at 350° F for 35 minutes.

Nut Loaf

Serves 4

1/2 cup	brazil nuts
1 cup each	almonds and sunflower seeds
1/4 cup	flax seed, ground
2-1/4 cups	water
2	small onions / diced (optional)
1/2 cup	fresh parsley
1/2 tsp ea	sage, thyme, salt, sweet basil
1/2 cup	almonds, ground
2 tbsp	arrowroot
dash	cayenne pepper
2 tbsp	oil
1/2 tsp	salt

1. Grind the brazil nuts, almonds and sunflower seeds in a blender or grinder.

2. In a separate bowl mix the flax seed and water until it reaches the consistency of an egg.

3. Combine the onions, parsley, sage, thyme salt and basil. Add the nut mixture, flax mixture and the onion mixture together and mix well.

4. Place the mixture in a well oiled loaf pan. Bake at 350° F for 25 minutes.

5. While the above loaf is baking, mix the almonds, water, arrowroot powder, cayenne, oil and salt with enough water to make thin sauce, together in a small saucepan.

6. Stir over medium heat until thick. Pour this mixture over the cooked loaf.

Three-Bean Loaf

...a great source of protein when served with rice

Serves 4 to 6

16 oz can	red kidney beans, drained
16 oz can	garbanzo beans, drained
1 cup	green beans, chopped and cooked
1 cup	celery, chopped
1/2 cup	onion, chopped
1 tsp	salt
1 tsp	cayenne
1	egg
1 tbsp	oil
3 tbsp	wheat germ
1 cup	tomato sauce (2 tomatoes liquified in a blender)

1. *Combine kidney and garbanzo beans, mash with potato masher.*

2. *Add green beans, celery, onion, salt, cayenne, egg, oil, wheat germ and 3 tbsp of tomato sauce, mix well.*

3. *Bake in an oiled loaf pan at 375° F for approximately 50 minutes.*

4. *This loaf will slice much easier if allowed to cool slightly.*

5. *Heat remaining tomato sauce and serve with or pour over.*

Lentil Dhal

...an East Indian favourite especially with the Pulao Rice

Serves 2 to 4

1 cup	brown lentils
1 large	onion, chopped
2	green peppers, chopped fine
3 tbsp	butter
1 tsp	turmeric
1 tsp	salt
1 tsp	dry mustard
1 tsp	coriander
1 tsp	cumin
pinch	cayenne

1. *Soak lentils in water for 1 hour; drain.*

2. *Sauté onion and peppers in butter until tender. Add lentils, turmeric and enough water to cover well.*

3. *Bring to boil, simmer until lentils are tender, adding more water if needed.*

4. *Add remainder of ingredients; mix well.*

5. *Should resemble thick soup. Some people like to puree it in the blender or with a potato masher.*

Pulao Rice

...yummy with the Lentil Dhal

Serves 4

1-1/4 cups	long grain rice
1/4 cup	butter
2	onions, sliced
3	cloves garlic, crushed
1-1/2 cups	peas
2-1/2 cups	hot water
1 tbsp	salt

1. Clean, wash and soak rice for half an hour.

2. Sauté onions in butter until transparent. Add drained rice, garlic and peas; continue to cook for 5 minutes, stirring.

3. Add hot water mix and bring to a boil. Simmer, covered, approximately 25 minutes, until liquid has been absorbed and rice is tender.

4. Add salt and more butter if desired.

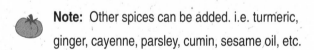 **Note:** Other spices can be added. i.e. turmeric, ginger, cayenne, parsley, cumin, sesame oil, etc.

Golden Saffron Rice

...a flavourful change from plain rice

Serves 4 to 6

3/4 cup	butter
1/4 tsp	cayenne pepper
1/2 tsp	saffron
1 tbsp	salt, or to taste
3 cups	long grain rice
6 cups	water or chicken broth
1 cup	cashews, broken
1 tbsp	sweet marjoram, chopped
1/4 cup	parsley, chopped
1/3 cup	lemon juice

1. *If saffron is in thread form rather than powdered, toast it in a small heavy skillet over medium heat until it is crisp and begins to darken. Cool and powder it with a pestle or back of a spoon.*

2. *Place butter, cayenne, saffron, salt, and water in saucepan and bring to a boil.*

3. *Add rice. Return to a boil. Reduce heat and cover. Cook 20 to 25 minutes for white rice, 35 to 40 minutes for brown.*

4. *Just before serving, add cashews, marjoram, parsley, and lemon juice.*

5. *Stir with a fork until well mixed.*

Frijoles (Refried Beans)

...great with the Guacamole from the Dressings section

Serves 6

1 lb	pinto beans, dried
1 large	onion, chopped
10 cups	water
6-8 tbsp	oil
1 tsp	salt
1/4 cup	hot sauce (see next page)

1. Cook beans in water with onion and 2 tbsp of the oil (simmering for approximately 1-1/2 hours).

2. Add salt, continue cooking for 15 minutes.

3. Drain and puree beans (or use a potato masher); fry in remaining oil until they are quite dry, add hot sauce and more salt if necessary, cook for 10 minutes.

Healthier Cleansing Tip: When using soup and sauce recipes that call for cream or whole milk, substitute them with cooked and pureed vegetables. This is also an excellent way of thickening without fat.

Hot Sauce

...the longer you cook it, the better it tastes

Makes approximately 10 cups

2 large	onions, chopped
1/2 bulb	garlic, crushed
9 cups	fresh tomatoes, chopped
1cup	fresh tomato paste (2 tomatoes liquified in a blender)
1 tbsp	basil
1 tbsp	thyme
1 tbsp	rosemary
1/2 tbsp	cumin
1/2 tbsp	cayenne
1 tbsp	oregano
2	bay leaves
2 tbsp	crushed dry chili
to taste	salt
to taste	jalapeno peppers (extremely hot, use fresh or canned)

Putting the Hot Sauce together is shown on the next page.

Putting the Hot Sauce Together

1. *Sauté the onions and garlic in butter until transparent, then add the rest of the ingredients.*

2. *We have only put suggested quantities for the spices, you can adjust them to your own taste preferences.*

3. *The longer you simmer this sauce the more flavour comes out of all the herbs and spices; minimum 45 minutes.*

If you use this recipe after the 12-day detox period you may add 1 to 2 tbsp of honey to curb any sharpness in taste.

The hot jalapeno peppers give an excellent flavour, but they are very hot; taste the sauce as you go along so as not to make it too strong.

Again, if you are using this recipe after the 12-day detox period and you find that the sauce does become too hot, we have found that eating it with guacamole or yogurt will help to cool your mouth.

 Note: You can make a large batch of this sauce and freeze it in small freezer bags; use it for spaghetti sauce, dip, gravy, etc.

Curried Lentils

...also great with Pulao Rice

Serves 4 to 6

1 large	sliced onion
2 tbsp	safflower oil
2 tbsp	mild curry powder (or to taste)
1 cup	carrots, sliced
2 cups	potatoes, diced
1 1/2 cups	water or vegetable broth
4 cups	cooked lentils, red or brown
1 cup	fresh parsley, minced (or 1/2 cup dried parsley)

1. *Sauté onion in oil. Stir in curry powder.*

2. *Add carrots and potatoes and continue stirring.*

3. *Gradually add water or broth. Bring to a boil, reduce heat and simmer 10 minutes or until vegetables are tender.*

4. *Add the lentils to the vegetables.*

5. *Sprinkle parsley on top before serving.*

Savoury Beans

...onions and spices make this basic vegetable very savoury!

Serves 5

1/2 lb	fresh snap beans, cut into 1" pieces
1 tsp	tarragon leaves
1/2 tsp	salt
1/8 tsp	ground black pepper
1 tbsp	lemon juice
1/2 lb	onions, sliced (2-1/2 cup)

1. *Place beans in saucepan containing 1" of boiling water, tarragon, salt, black pepper and lemon juice.*

2. *Cook uncovered for <u>only</u> 5 minutes.*

3. *Add onions. Reduce heat and simmer, covered for 5 minutes or until beans are tender.*

Healthier Cleansing Tip: *Green beans are high in fibre, chlorophyll, Vitamin A, Vitamin C and calcium.*

Blushed Cauliflower

...this simple dish tastes as wonderful as it looks!

Serves 4

1 medium	cauliflower head
1 tsp	tarragon leaves, crumbled
1/2 tsp	salt
1/16 tsp	ground white pepper
1/2 tsp	paprika

1. *Wash cauliflower thoroughly; remove outer leaves and core, keeping head intact.*

2. *Boil one inch of water in a large saucepan or skillet. Add tarragon, salt and white pepper.*

3. *Add the cauliflower head and cook for 10 minutes basting frequently with the tarragon flavoured liquid.*

4. *Cover, reduce heat and simmer 15 to 20 minutes longer or until tender.*

5. *Carefully remove cauliflower to serving dish. Dust with paprika.*

6. *Serve immediately.*

 Healthier Cleansing Tip: *Remember it is best to eat vegetables raw or lightly steamed, to retain their nutrients.*

Sophisticated Vegetables

...this dish can be served cold or slightly warmed.

Serves 4

2 cups	string beans, lightly steamed, cold and chopped
1/2 cup	water chestnuts, sliced
1 cup	cauliflower, lightly steamed and sliced thin
2 tbsp	red onion, diced
1/2 cup	beets, lightly steamed and sliced thin
1 tsp	salt
1/4 cup	lemon juice
1/3 cup	sesame oil
1/4 tsp	garlic powder

1. *Combine all ingredients and mix together well. Serve.*

 Healthier Cleansing Tip: *Cauliflower, together with broccoli, kale, rutabaga, brussel sprouts, cabbage, kohlrabi and mustard greens, is a member of the Cruciferous family of vegetables which are well known for their health-giving benefits. It is high in potassium, fibre, Vitamin C and folic acid.*

Neapolitan Zucchini

A delicious addition to brown rice.

Serves 4

1 lb	zucchini squash
3 cups	fresh tomatoes, chopped
1 tsp	oregano leaves, crushed
1 tsp	onion, minced
1/2 tsp	salt
1/2 tsp	garlic powder
1/4 tsp	black pepper, coarsely ground

1. *Slice squash crosswise into 1/2 inch thick rounds.*

2. *In a medium size saucepan combine squash with remaining ingredients.*

3. *Cook, covered, over medium heat until squash is tender, about 15 minutes.*

 Healthier Cleansing Tip: *Zucchini is a member of the Summer Squash family. It is a highly versatile vegetable that can be stuffed and baked, sauteed, steamed, or grilled. Zucchinis are high in Vitamin A.*

Gado-Gado Sauce

...an Indonesian dish with spicy tahini sauce.

Makes approximately 4 cups of sauce

2 tbsp	sesame oil
1 cup	onions, chopped
2 cloves	garlic, chopped
1 to 2 tsp	freshly grated ginger
1	bay leaf
1 cup	tahini
1/4 tsp	cayenne
juice of	1 lemon (optional)
1 tsp	salt
3 cups	water
	assorted vegetables

1. Sauté the onion, garlic, ginger and bay leaf in the sesame oil.

2. Add the tahini, cayenne, lemon juice, salt, water and mix thoroughly. Simmer for 30 minutes.

3. This sauce goes over an arrangement of cooked and raw vegetables. Arrange a bed of shredded cabbage for a base.

4. Then add a mixture of steamed broccoli spears, steamed whole green beans, mung bean sprouts, steamed cauliflower, steamed potatoes, steamed cabbage. (This recipe can have tofu, sauteed in oil with sesame seeds, added to the veggies after the 12-day detox program .)

Hurry-Up Hearty Hash Patties

...yummy for Sunday breakfast

Serves 4

1/2 cup	celery, chopped
1/2 cup	nuts (almonds or walnuts), chopped
2	eggs
2 tbsp	oil of your choice
1/2 tsp	salt
1 clove	garlic, pressed (optional)
2 cups	potatoes, cooked and grated

or

2 cups	beans, cooked and mashed

1. *Combine all the ingredients in a bowl.*

2. *Form patties from the mixture and sauté them in a lightly oiled skillet until browned on both sides.*

Falafel -- Middle Eastern Dish

Makes 6 cups

2 cups	garbanzo beans (soaked overnight)
1/2 cup	cold water
1 tbsp	safflower oil
1 clove	garlic (or to taste), chopped
2 tbsp	parsley, minced
1/4 tsp	cayenne
1 cup	green onion, minced

1. Grind or mash 1/3 cup soaked garbanzos.

2. In a blender, blend the remaining 2/3 cup soaked garbanzos with 1/2 cup cold water until very fine.

3. Add the chopped garlic, minced parsley, and cayenne to the blender and blend again.

4. Now add the blended garbanzo mixture to ground or mashed garbanzos and mix well. (This gives two different garbanzo consistencies in one!)

5. Shape the mixture into balls. Place on ungreased baking pan. Cover with foil.

6. Bake at 350° F covered for 15 minutes. Turn. Bake uncovered 10 minutes.

7. Serve with sprinkled green onion and hot sauce (see Hot Sauce on page 56).

or

1. Spread mixture to 1/2 inch thickness on a greased cookie sheet.

2. Bake covered 15 minutes. Uncovered 15 minutes. Cut into squares.

Sunflower Seed Wedge

...another tasty snack, or a meal served with a big leafy salad.

Serves 4

1 cup	carrot, grated
1 cup	celery, chopped
1 tsp	onion, minced (optional)
1/2 tsp	salt
1 tsp	basil
1 cup	sunflower seed butter or almond butter
1/4 cup	sunflower seeds, toasted

1. *Combine all ingredients in a large bowl.*

2. *Pat into an 8" pie plate and sprinkle sunflower seeds on top.*

3. *Refrigerate until mixture hardens. Cut into wedges and serve.*

Veggie Nut Loaf

...any of the nut loaves can be sliced for a topping on rice cakes as a quick and tasty lunch.

Serves 4-6

1 cup	carrots, grated
1 cup	tomatoes, diced
1 cup	celery, grated
1/2 cup	green pepper, grated
2 tbsp	oil of your choice
1 clove	garlic, minced (optional)
1 cup	ground nuts and seeds to hold it together
to taste	salt

1. *Combine all ingredients in large bowl.*

2. *Mold into an oiled serving dish. Top with sprouts.*

3. *Chill until firm and slice.*

 Healthier Cleansing Tip: *The Veggie Nut Loaf, rich in protein, is an excellent alternatives to plain vegetables. It enables you to jazz up raw vegetables and benefit from their health-giving properties.*

Millet Sunflower Carrot Casserole

...a quick, delicious meal that can be easily stored in the refrigerator and reheated for lunches.

Serves 8

1 lb	turkey, ground
1/2 cup	onion, chopped
1/2 cup	celery, chopped
1 clove	garlic, minced
4 cups	carrots or parsnips, thickly sliced
3 cups	fresh tomatoes, chopped
1/2 tsp	salt
1 cup	hulled millet
1/2 cup	sunflower seeds or chopped almonds

1. *Brown meat with onion, celery and garlic.*

2. *Place the meat mixture in a 2 litre baking dish and add the carrots, tomatoes, salt, millet and seeds or nuts. Toss together.*

3. *Bake at 300° F for 1 hour or until millet is tender.*

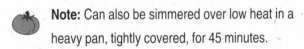 **Note:** Can also be simmered over low heat in a heavy pan, tightly covered, for 45 minutes.

Baked Stuffed Fish

...a delicious meal for the whole family

Serves 6

3 to 5 lbs	whole fish: bass, bluefish, cod, haddock
1/4 cup	oil
1/4 cup	celery, finely chopped
1/4 cup	onion, finely chopped
1/2 cup	chicken broth or Bernard Jensen Broth and Seasoning Mix
1 1/2 cups	rice or millet, cooked

1. *Clean the fish. Sauté the onion and celery in oil until lightly browned.*

2. *Add rice (or millet) and broth and blend together until well mixed. Stuff the fish with this mixture, not more that 2/3 full.*

3. *Close the opening with skewers or toothpicks laced together with string. Put fish on an oiled, ovenproof platter or on oiled unglazed paper in a shallow baking pan.*

4. *Cut 3 or 4 slits through the skin on each side to keep the fish from falling apart during baking.*

5. *Bake at 400° F for 30 to 45 minutes, or until flaky.*

6. *To serve, make a deep cut along the backbone, then cut in pieces at right angles to the backbone.*

Lemon Broiled Chicken

Lemon juice and ginger make this simple to prepare meal delicious.

Serves 6

1/4 cup	lemon juice
1 tsp	grated lemon peel
1 tsp	salad oil
1/2 tsp	salt
1/2 tsp ea	ground ginger, paprika
1/4 tsp	onion powder
1/4 tsp	ground black pepper
2 1/2 lbs	broiler-fryer chicken, quartered

1. *In a small bowl, combine lemon juice and peel, oil, salt, ginger, paprika, onion powder and black pepper; mix well.*

2. *Brush over chicken. Place chicken on broiler pan. Broil 7 to 9 inches from heat source for 10 minutes.*

3. *Turn chicken. Continue broiling, turning and basting occasionally, until brown and crisp, about 25 minutes longer.*

 Healthier Cleansing Tip: *Meat recipes have been included for non-vegetarians. Organic meats and wild fish are best as they do not contain the hormones and antibiotics often found in farmed meats.*

Curried Turkey Thighs

Serves 6

3	turkey thighs (1-1/2 lbs each)
1 tsp	salt
1/2 tsp	pepper
1-2 tbsp	oil
3/4 tsp	curry powder
1/4 tsp	ginger powder
1-1/2 cups	water
3	bouillon cubes or 2 tsp Bernard Jensen Broth Mix
1-1/2 tbsp	arrowroot
1 tsp	lemon juice

1. Season thighs with salt and pepper. In a heavy skillet, brown meat slowly on both sides in heated oil, using just enough to prevent sticking.

2. Add the curry and ginger powder and sauté slowly for five minutes. Stir in the water and seasoning.

3. Cover and let simmer 1-3/4 to 2 hours, until turkey is tender. Remove turkey and keep warm.

4. Skim off and discard any surface fat from juices. Blend arrowroot with 2 tablespoons cold water. Stir into liquid remaining in pan.

5. Cook, stirring until sauce boils and thickens slightly. Stir in lemon juice.

6. Serve turkey with thickened pan juices on the side.

Fish Fillets Almandine

...a refreshingly light entree

Serves 4 to 6

1/4 cup	oil
3 tbsp	slivered almonds
1-1/2 - 2 lbs	fish fillets, snapper, cod or sole
1 tbsp	lemon, lime or pineapple juice
1/2 tsp	garlic salt
1/4 tsp	pepper

1. Heat 2 tbsp of oil in a large skillet. Add the 3 tbsp of almonds and cook over medium low heat 2 to 3 minutes until golden brown, stirring constantly. Remove almonds and set aside.

2. In remaining oil, cook fish 3 to 4 minutes on each side until fish flakes when pierced with a fork.

3. Remove to a warm platter and season with salt and pepper.

4. Stir lemon juice, garlic salt and pepper into pan drippings with almonds.

5. Spoon this mixture over fish and serve.

Herbed Baked Fish Steak

While you are on your Herbal D-Tox program you can be assured that your dinner guests will enjoy this dish, too!

Serves 4

1-1/2 lbs	fresh halibut steak or other fish
1/4 cup	onion, minced
1 tsp	powdered mustard
1/2 tsp	oregano leaves
1/4 tsp	marjoram leaves
1/2 tsp	salt
1/16 tsp	ground black pepper
4 tsp	lemon juice
pinch	paprika

1. *Wipe fish with damp cloth and arrange in baking dish.*

2. *Combine minced onion, mustard, oregano, marjoram, salt and black pepper with 2 tsp water; let stand 10 minutes for flavours to blend.*

3. *Add lemon juice. Spoon mixture evenly over fish.*

4. *Bake uncovered in a very hot preheated oven (475° F) 17 to 20 minutes, or until fish flakes easily with a fork.*

5. *Garnish with paprika. Serve with a lemon wedge, if desired.*

 ooking Grains

Grain (1 cup)	Water (cups)	Time
Barley		
Hulled (not peeled)	3	60 min
Natural brown	3	90 min
Flakes	2	10 min
Buckwheat groats	2	20 min
Kasha		
Hulled	2	20 min
Bulgur		
Coarse, med or fine	2	15 - 30 min
Cornmeal		
Yellow	3	15 - 30 min
White	3	15 - 30 min
Millet	2	30 - 40 min
Oats		
Rolled/flaked oatmeal	2	10 min
Steel-cut	2	10 min
Rice - unpolished brown		
Short grain	2	30 - 40 min
Long grain	2	35 - 45 min
Creamed rice	3	25 min
Rye		
Whole kernels	2 1/2	1hr/10min
Flaked	2	20 min
Wheat		
Berries	2 1/2	90 min
Flakes	2	15 - 20 min
Cracked wheat	3	25 min
Porridge	5 1/2	2-1/2 hrs

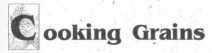ooking Grains

Makes	Pressure Cooking	
	Water	**Time**
3	2 1/2	40 min
3	2 1/2	50 min
2	no	
2	no	
2	no	
2	no	
2	no	
2	no	
2 1/2	2	20 min
2	no	
2	no	
2	1 1/2	15 min
2	1 1/2	15-20 min
4	no	
3	2	50 min
2	no	
3	2	50 min
2	no	
2	no	
3 1/2	no	

Note: Season with 1/4 tsp sea salt per cup of dry grain.

Notes to Remember...

_____

_____

_____

_____

_____

_____

_____

_____

_____

_____

_____

_____

_____

_____

_____

_____